More Adventures of the
SUPERKIDS

D1529674

STUDENT BOOK UNITS 7–8

Name

FIRST GRADE

More Adventures of the
SUPERKIDS

BY PLEASANT T. ROWLAND

ILLUSTRATED BY LORETTA LUSTIG, MERYL HENDERSON & DOUG ROY

CONTRIBUTING WRITER: VALERIE TRIPP

DEVELOPED BY ROWLAND READING FOUNDATION

For the convenience of teachers and parents, this book contains abbreviated citations of the Common Core State Standards, noted in pink at the bottom of each page. The complete standards are available online at *superkidsreading.org*.

ISBN: 978-1-61436-228-9   MO36228.0315   2 3 4 5 6 4495 19 18 17 16 15

UNITS   1–2   3–4   5–6   7–8   9–10

Parents: Your child underlined ar, or, or ear in the words in the boxes, read the words aloud, and circled the picture that each word names.

Unit 7

Trickers

Sometimes ar, or, and ear are like er.

ar   or   ear

1. dollar

4. worm

7. learn

2. collar

5. tractor

8. pearl

3. calendar

6. doctor

9. search

1

er	er	er	er	er
coll**ar**	may**or**	h**ear**d	doll**ar**s	s**ear**ched

_____

1. Sal _____ a dog bark.

_____

2. The dog had no _____ .

_____

3. Sal _____ for the dog's home.

_____

4. The dog belonged to the _____ .

_____

5. The mayor gave Sal ten _____
   to thank him.

Parents: Your child underlined *ar*, *or*, or *ear* in the words at the top of the page and then wrote those words on the lines to complete the sentences about the pictures.

2

Come to my slumber party!
It's on June 5, so mark your
calendar. Come at six and bring
a sleeping bag. But don't worry,
we won't go to bed early! We'll
stay up late, tell tales, learn some
word games, and have lots of fun.

See you then,
Tic

world

earth

dollar

Trickers
ar, or, ear=er

ar

collar
dollar
forward
backward

or

word
worm
world

ear

earn
earth
early

Phonics, Spelling, Vocabulary
RF.1.3, L.1.2d, L.1.2e, L.1.4

1. What kind of story did Tic tell?
   ○ a funny animal story
   ○ a story about real life
   ○ a creepy monster story

2. Why did Tic grab Lily?
   ○ She was helping Lily stand up.
   ○ She was acting like a monster.
   ○ She was mad at Lily.

3. Why didn't Lily like Tic's story?
   ○ It made her afraid.
   ○ It was too sad.
   ○ It was long and boring.

4. What was wiggling by Lily's sleeping bag?
   ○ a monster
   ○ Tic's feet
   ○ a kitten

5. What helped Lily feel better?
   ○ telling jokes
   ○ going inside to sleep
   ○ looking at the stars

Comprehension
RL.1.1, RL.1.10, SL.1.1

Parents: Your child read sentences that characters from "Slumber Party" could have said and filled in the bubble next to the -ly word that tells how the character would have said the words.

 **How would they say the words?**

1. "It will be fun to sleep outside," Tic said _____.

   ○ sadly   ○ cheerfully

2. "Who stole my pot of silver?" the monster asked _____.

   ○ angrily   ○ sleepily

3. "Oh, Lily, what is the matter?" Tic asked _____.

   ○ joyfully   ○ kindly

4. "I'm afraid of the dark," Lily said _____.

   ○ happily   ○ unhappily

5. "I know how to make you feel better," Tic said _____.

   ○ helpfully   ○ meanly

6. "I like the way the stars sparkle," Lily said _____.

   ○ angrily   ○ happily

5

Comprehension; Grammar, Usage, and Mechanics
RL.1.3, RL.1.9, L.1.1

1.

bird   heard   card

2.

learn   star   turn

3.

dollar   doctor   corn

4.

shirt   worm   alarm

5.

worry   hurry   farm

6.

jar   tractor   burger

7.

burn   barn   earn

8.

car   curl   twirl

Parents: Your child read each sentence about the story "The Runaway Dragon" and then filled in the bubble next to the word that has almost the same meaning as the pink word in the sentence.

Which word means the same as the pink word?

1. Oswald was working on a big project.

   ○ task   ○ tickle   ○ nap

2. The dragon had a horrible red grin with big teeth.

   ○ pretty   ○ terrific   ○ awful

3. The box slipped out of Hot Rod's hands.

   ○ closed   ○ fell   ○ rattled

4. The dragon dipped and twirled up in the sky.

   ○ hugged   ○ slept   ○ spun

5. The dragon's long green tail flapped in the wind.

   ○ waved   ○ sang   ○ dripped

6. "Oh, my pretty bird!" squawked the parrot.

   ○ smelly   ○ fluffy   ○ good-looking

7

Comprehension, Vocabulary
RL.1.1, L.1.5

Parents: On this page and page 9, your child read and followed directions that checked your child's understanding of the story "The Runaway Dragon."

1. Put a green X on the dragon's flashing eye.

2. Put a black X on the dragon's horrible red grin.

3. Draw a line under the person who made the dragon.

4. Put a purple X on the black box that made the dragon fly.

5. Who dropped the black box? Mark him with a blue check.

Pretty bird!

6. Who has a pet parrot? Draw a line from him to the parrot.

7. What did Polly call the dragon? Draw two lines under her words.

8. Fill in the bubble by the words that tell what the dragon did over Main Street:

   ○ sang and laughed   ○ ate and drank   ○ dipped and dived

9. Who saved the dragon? Mark her with a red check.

Comprehension
RL.1.1

1. First, _____

2. Next, _____

3. Then, _____

4. Then, _____

The end!

Writing, Vocabulary, Comprehension
W.1.3, W.1.5, L.1.6, L.1.4, RL.1.7

ow

cow
brown
frown

Unit 8

owl
crown
howl

Parents: Your child underlined ow in the words at the top of the page and then traced and wrote letters to complete ow words that tell about the pictures.

1. Ow!

fl___er

2. Ow!

d___n

3. Ow!

cr___d

4. Ow!

c___boy

5. Grrr! Ow!

gr___l

6. Ow!

cl___n

11

Phonemic Awareness, Phonics
RF.1.2c, RF.1.3

ouch

Parents: Your child underlined ou in the words at the top of the page and then traced and wrote letters to complete phrases with ou words that tell about the pictures.

<u>o</u>uch	f<u>ou</u>nd	m<u>ou</u>th
<u>ou</u>t	p<u>ou</u>ch	sh<u>ou</u>t

1. a r___ nd cl___ d

2. a gr___ ch on a c___ ch

3. a th___ sand tr___ t

12

Parents: Your child traced and wrote letters to complete rhyming ou and ow words.

1. grouch

p _ _ _ _

c _ _ _ _ _

2. tower

sh _ _ _ _

fl _ _ _ _ _

3. found

p _ _ _ _

r _ _ _ _ _

4. frown

br _ _ _

cl _ _ _ _

5. out

tr _ _ _

sh _ _ _

Wait for me!

6. howl

Grrr!

gr _ _ _

_ _ _ _

13

snow

low
show

grow
blow

yellow
own

1. wind _ _

2. thr _ _

3. sl _ _

slow

4. sn___ man _ _

5. cr___ _ _

6. shad___ _ _

Phonemic Awareness, Phonics, Vocabulary
RF.1.2c, RF.1.2b, RF.1.3, L.1.4

Memory Words

Parents: Your child listened to a CD and learned the Memory Words at the top of this page.

warm   walk   give   once   done

Music can be warm.
Music can be happy.
Music can be slow.
Music can be snappy.

Music makes you walk.
Music makes you fly.
Music makes you laugh.
Music makes you cry.

Give all you can give,
When you play a song.
Make the music loud,
Make the music strong.

If you try it once,
You'll see that music is fun.
Once you start a tune,
You never will be done.

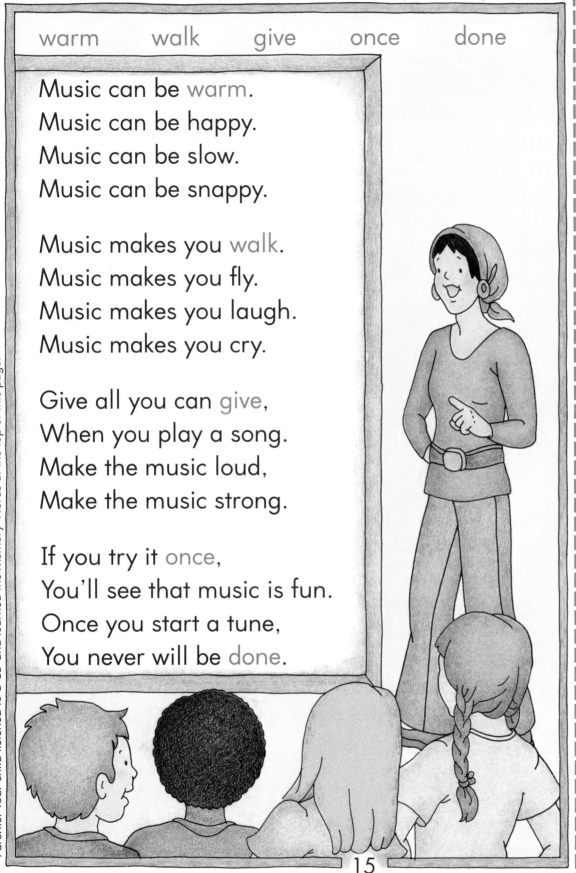

Parents: Help your child memorize the spelling of these Memory Words. Each word will be on the Unit 8 spelling test.

warm

walk

give

once

done

Vocabulary, Spelling
L.1.4, RF.1.3g, L.1.2d

Pattern Words

Parents: Help your child practice spelling words that follow a pattern. Five of these words will be on the Unit 8 spelling test.

oud

loud

proud

ound

found

round

sound

ow = Ow!

own

town

brown

frown

ow = ō

ow

grow

slow

snow

1. Hot Rod has been grouchy.

   ○ grumpy   ○ crunchy   ○ candy

2. The kids heard someone play a tune.

   ○ game   ○ song   ○ trick

3. Hot Rod wants to quit his clarinet lessons.

   ○ quick   ○ stop   ○ spot

4. The hall was getting warm. Alf began to squirm.

   ○ wiggle   ○ squeal   ○ yell

5. Icky asks if it's hard to play a clarinet.

   ○ easy   ○ difficult   ○ loud

16

Vocabulary, Phonics, Spelling
L.1.4, L.1.5, RF.1.2b, RF.1.3, L.1.d, L.1.2e

1. Why did Hot Rod want to quit his clarinet lessons?

○ The lessons cost too much.

○ Playing the clarinet is hard.

○ He likes playing drums better.

2. Why did Cass make the kids go to the talent show?

○ to hear Hot Rod play clarinet

○ to see the funny animal acts

○ to help them plan their own talent show

3. What did the kids think of Hot Rod's clarinet playing?

○ It was very funny.

○ It was really awful.

○ It was really good.

4. What was Hot Rod's plan at the end of the story?

○ to fix his broken clarinet

○ to take more clarinet lessons

○ to quit taking clarinet lessons

5. What lesson did Hot Rod learn in the story?

○ Always put away your toys.

○ Help others whenever you can.

○ Don't give up when things get hard.

Parents: Your child answered questions about the story "The Lesson" by filling in the bubble next to the correct answer for each question.

17

Comprehension
RL.1.1, RL.1.10, SL.1.1

1. Costumes

growl

owl

2. Dog sounds

bow-wow

cowboy

3. Animals

cow

clown

4. Grouchy looks

snow

ow

5. Soft things

pillow

ouch

6. Words to say when it hurts

pout

frown

Parents: The words above the handwriting lines describe categories. For each category, your child identified two words from the list on the right that belong in that category and wrote those words under the name of the category.

Vocabulary
L.1.5a

⭐

walk

⭐

⭐

⭐

warm

⭐

⭐

Parents: Your child traced or wrote Memory Words on cards, cut out the cards, and used them to play a game called "Match It!"

⭐

done

Match it!

⭐

⭐

give

⭐

⭐

⭐

once

⭐

⭐

once   once   once

give   give   give

warm   warm   warm

done   done   done

walk   walk   walk

Parents: Your child completed each sentence to explain why something happened in the story "That Was Yesterday."

1. Alf got mad at Frits because _____

_____

_____

2. The tag game ended because _____

_____

_____

3. The kids didn't want Frits and Alf to come fishing because

_____

_____

_____

_____

4. Alf and Frits started speaking to each other again because

_____

_____

_____

_____

Comprehension
RL.1.1, RL.1.10, SL.1.1

Put 1 next to what happens first.
Put 2 next to what happens second.
Put 3 next to what happens third.

☐ Frits says Alf is It now and Alf says he is not.

☐ Alf and Frits begin pushing each other.

☐ Frits reaches out to tag Alf in the game.

☐ The rest of the kids go home.

☐ Frits and Alf quit playing and go home.

☐ The kids pull Alf and Frits apart.

☐ The kids go fishing and Alf and Frits stay on the bus.

☐ Alf shows Frits the plans for making a skateboard.

☐ Alf reads a comic as he sits on the bus.

☐ Alf tells Sal that he and Frits are working on a super project.

☐ Alf and Frits get off the bus to go get Frits's skates.

☐ Alf and Frits bump into Sal outside.

Parents: Your child numbered the sentences in each group 1, 2, or 3 to show the order of events in the story "That Was Yesterday."

22

Parents: Your child drew a smile or a frown on the face by each word to show if the word tells about something unhappy or happy. Then your child wrote an unhappy word and a happy word beside the faces at the bottom.

unhappy words

frown

happy words

smile

1. grouchy

2. grand

3. horrible

4. Hurray!

5. scowl

6. helpful

7. laugh

8. pals

9. nasty

10. pout

11. cheerful

12. gladly

13. cheater

14. mean

15. joyful

16. _____

17. _____

23

Vocabulary
L.1.5a

Pals Forever

If you get mad at a pal, don't shout!

Don't frown, scowl, or pout.

And never, ever throw a punch!

Tell your pal how you feel.

Find a way to work things out.

Before you know it, the two of you

will laugh and clown around again!

Parents: Your child read a poster about friendship, circled words with ou and ow, and then wrote each circled word in the column under the word that has the same sound for ou or ow.

c<u>ou</u>ch

<u>ow</u>l

sn<u>ow</u>

Phonics, Comprehension, Spelling
RF.1.3, RI.1.1, RI.1.7, L.1.2d

Parents: Your child answered questions about what could have happened differently in the story "That Was Yesterday."

What happened?	What could have happened?
You missed me by a mile.	1. What if Frits had said, "Maybe you're right, Alf. I may have missed you"?
You can both just stay here!	2. What if Alf and Frits went on the fishing trip?
Look at this skateboard!	3. What if Frits had ripped up the comic?

25

Comprehension
RL.1.1

ISBN 978-1-61436-228-9

9 781614 362289   90000